MICROBIOLOGY ANATOMY COLORING BOOK

SCAN THE CODE TO ACCESS YOUR FREE DIGITAL COPY

THIS BOOK BELONGS TO

_____

TABLE OF CONTENTS

SECTION 1: PLANT CELL

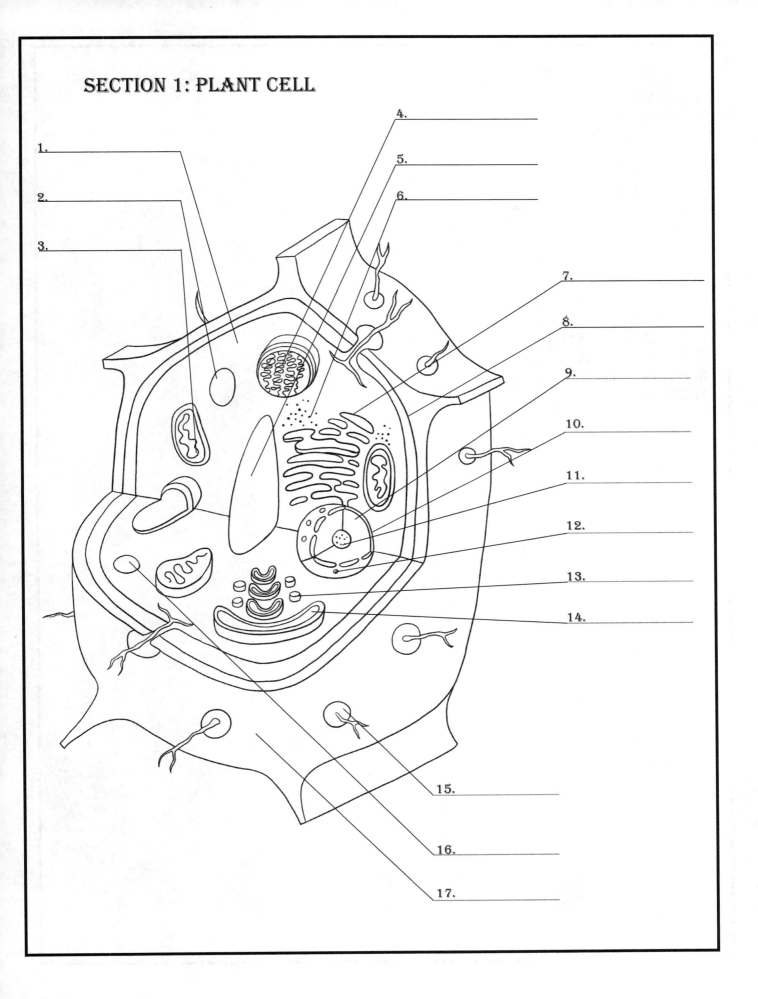

1.

2.

3.

4.

5.

6.

7.

8.

9.

10.

11.

12.

13.

14.

15.

16.

17.

SECTION 1: PLANT CELL

1. CYTOPLASM
2. LYSOSOME
3. MITOCHONDRION
4. CHLOROPLAST
5. VACUOLE
6. RIBOSOMES
7. ENDOPLASMIC RETICULUM
8. CELL MEMBRANE
9. NUCLEOPLASM
10. NUCLEAR ENVELOPE
11. NUCLEOUS
12. NUCLEAR PORE
13. VESICLE
14. GOLGI APPARATUS
15. PLASMODESMA
16. PEROXISOME
17. CELL WALL

SECTION 2: ANIMAL CELL

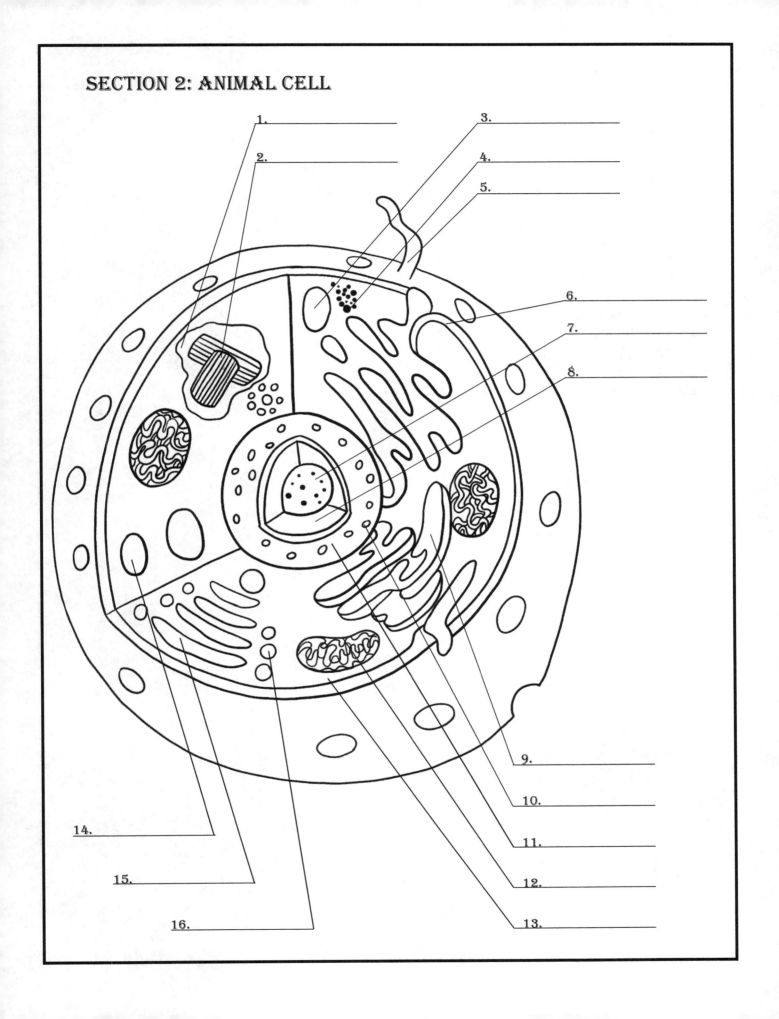

1.

2.

3.

4.

5.

6.

7.

8.

9.

10.

11.

12.

13.

14.

15.

16.

SECTION 2: ANIMAL CELL

1. CENTROSOME
2. CENTRIOLE
3. LYSOSOME
4. RIBOSOMES
5. CILIUM
6. CELL MEMBRANE
7. NUCLEOUS
8. NUCLEOPLASM
9. ENDOPLASMIC RETICULUM
10. NUCLEAR PORE
11. NUCLEAR ENVELOPE
12. MITOCHONDRION
13. CYTOPLASM
14. PEROXISOME
15. GOLGI APPARATUS
16. SECRETORY VESICLES

SECTION 3: MITOSIS

2. _____

1. _____

3. _____

6. _____

4. _____

5. _____

SECTION 3: MITOSIS

1. PROPHASE
2. PROMETHAPHASE
3. METAPHASE
4. ANAPHASE
5. TELOPHASE
6. CYTOKINESIS

SECTION 4: MEIOSIS

1. _____

2. _____

3. _____

4. _____

5. _____

6. _____

7. _____

8. _____

9. _____

10. _____

11. _____

12. _____

13. _____

SECTION 4: MEIOSIS

1. MEIOSIS I
2. INTERPHASE
3. PROPHASE I
4. METAPHASE I
5. ANAPHASE I
6. TELOPHASE I
7. CYTOKINESIS I
8. MEIOSIS II
9. PROPHASE II
10. METAPHASE II
11. ANAPHASE II
12. TELOPHASE II
13. CYTOKINESIS II

SECTION 5: BACTERIA CELL

GENERALIZED STRUCTURE OF BACTERIUM

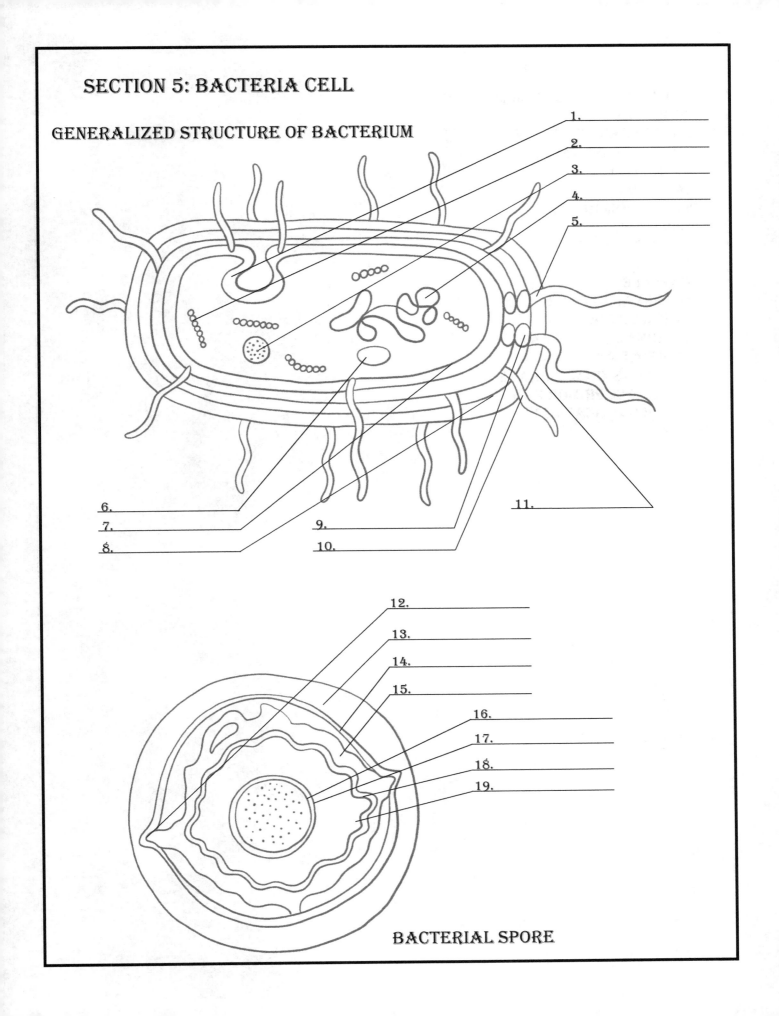

1. _____
2. _____
3. _____
4. _____
5. _____

6. _____
7. _____
8. _____
9. _____
10. _____
11. _____

12. _____
13. _____
14. _____
15. _____
16. _____
17. _____
18. _____
19. _____

BACTERIAL SPORE

SECTION 5: BACTERIA CELL

1. INFOLDING OF PLASMA MEMBRANE
2. RIBOSOMES
3. CYTOPLASMIC INCLUSION
4. DNA COILED INTO NUCLEOID
5. FLAGELLUM
6. PLASMOID DNA
7. PLASMA MEMBRANE
8. CELL WALL
9. BASAL BODY
10. PILI
11. CAPSULE
12. GERMINAL GROOVE
13. OUTER SPORE COAT
14. INTERNAL SPORE COAT
15. SUBCOAT MATERIAL
17. CYTOPLASMIC MEMBRANE
17. CELL WALL PRIMORDIUM
18. OUTER CORTICAL LAYER
19. CORTEX

SECTION 6: BACTERIA TYPES AND ARRANGEMENTS

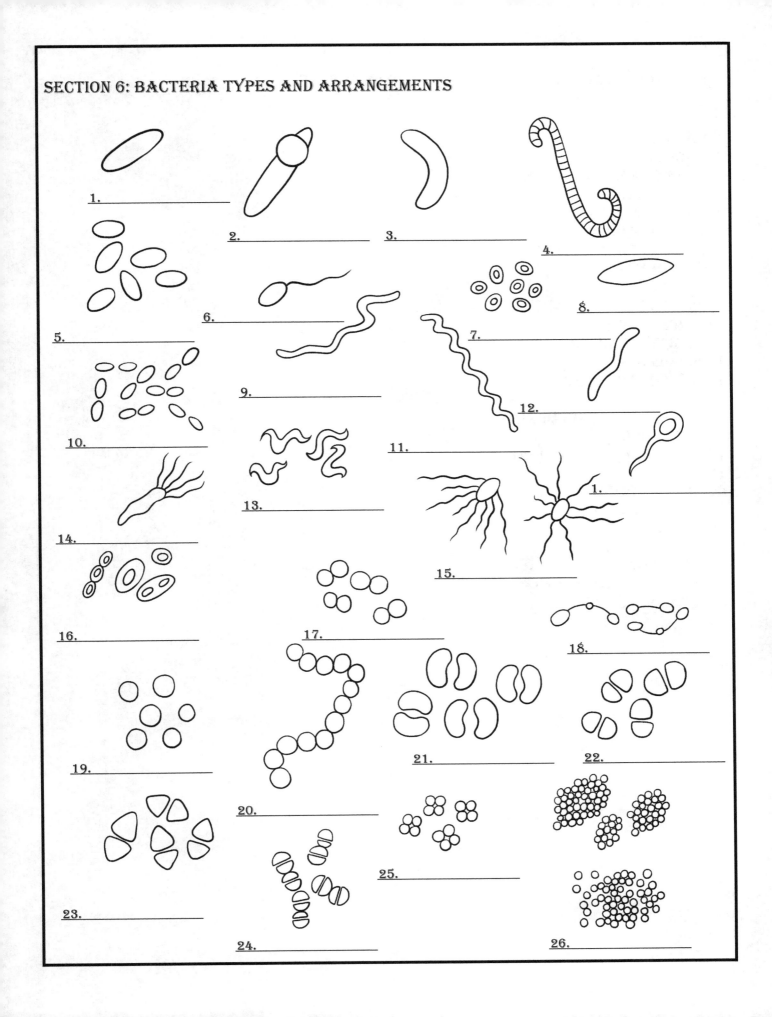

1. _____

2. _____

3. _____

4. _____

5. _____

6. _____

7. _____

8. _____

9. _____

10. _____

11. _____

12. _____

13. _____

14. _____

15. _____

16. _____

17. _____

18. _____

19. _____

20. _____

21. _____

22. _____

23. _____

24. _____

25. _____

26. _____

SECTION 6: BACTERIA TYPES AND ARRANGEMENTS

1. BACILLUS
2. BACILLUS WITH SUB-TERMINAL SPORE
3. COMA SHAPED BACILLUS (VIBRIO)
4. LEPTOSPIRA
5. BACILLI IN CLUSTER
6. VIBRIO CHLOREALE
7. BORTTADELLA PERTUSSIS
8. FUSIFORM
9. BORRELIA
10. DIPLOBACCILI
11. TREPONEMA
12. CAMPYLOBACTER
13. SPIRILLA
14. HELICOBACTER PYLORI
15. E-COLI
16. KLEBISIELLA PNEUMONIAE
17. DIPLOCOCCI
18. NEISSERIA GONORRHOEAE
19. COCCI
20. STEREPTOCOCCI
21. GONOCOCCI
22. MENINGOCOCCI
23. PNEUMOCOCCI
24. NEISSERIA
25. GAFFKYA TETRAGENA
26. STEPHYLOCOCCI

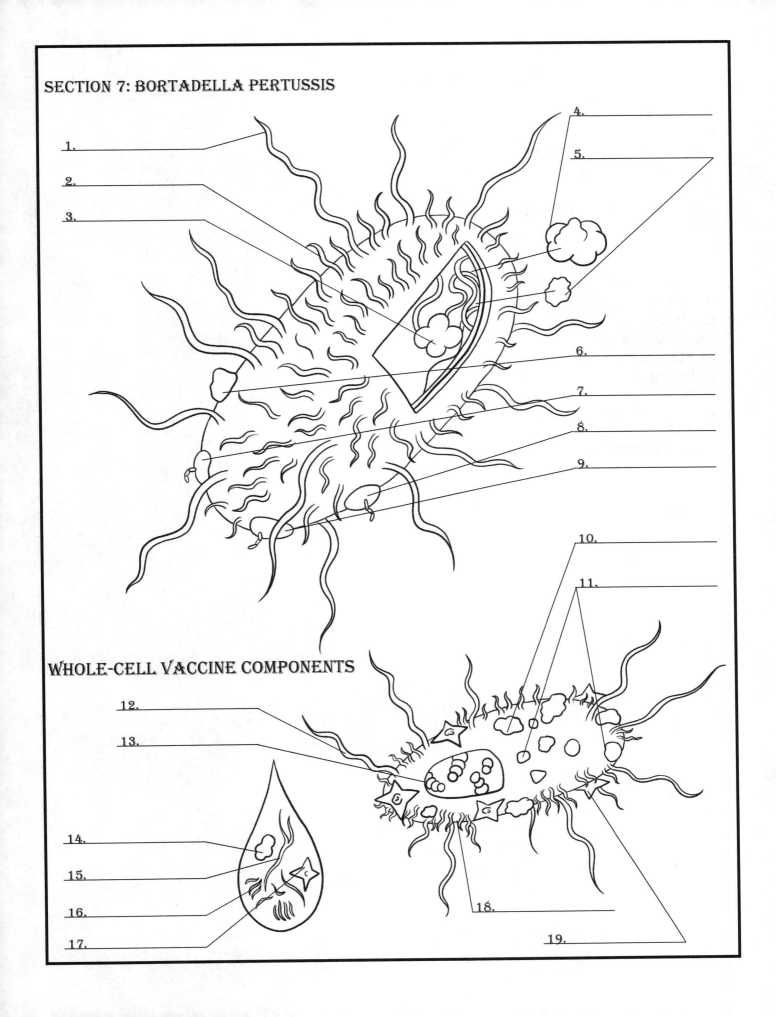

SECTION 7: BORTADELLA PERTUSSIS

1.
2.
3.
4.
5.
6.
7.
8.
9.
10.
11.

WHOLE-CELL VACCINE COMPONENTS

12.
13.
14.
15.
16.
17.
18.
19.

SECTION 7: BORTADELLA PERTUSSIS

1. FIMBRIE
2. FHA
3. DERMONECROTIC TOXIN
4. PERTUSSIS TOXIN
5. TCT
6. ADENYLATE CYCLASE TOXIN
7. PERTACTIN
8. TCF
9. BRKA
10. PERTACTIN
11. TOXINS
12. FIMBRIAE
13. ENDO-TOXINS
14. PERTACTIN
15. FIMBRIAE
16. FHA
17. PERTUSSIS TOXIN
18. FHA
19. PERTUSSIS TOXIN

SECTION 8: MYCOBACTERIUM TUBERCULOSIS

1.

2.

3.

4.

5.

6.

7.

8.

SECTION 8: MYCOBACTERIUM TUBERCULOSIS

1. PILI
2. BACTERIAL FLAGELLUM
3. PLASMID RIBOSOME
4. RIBOSOME
5. PLASMA MEMBRANE
6. CELL WALL
7. CAPSULE
8. NUCLEOID (CIRCULAR DNA)

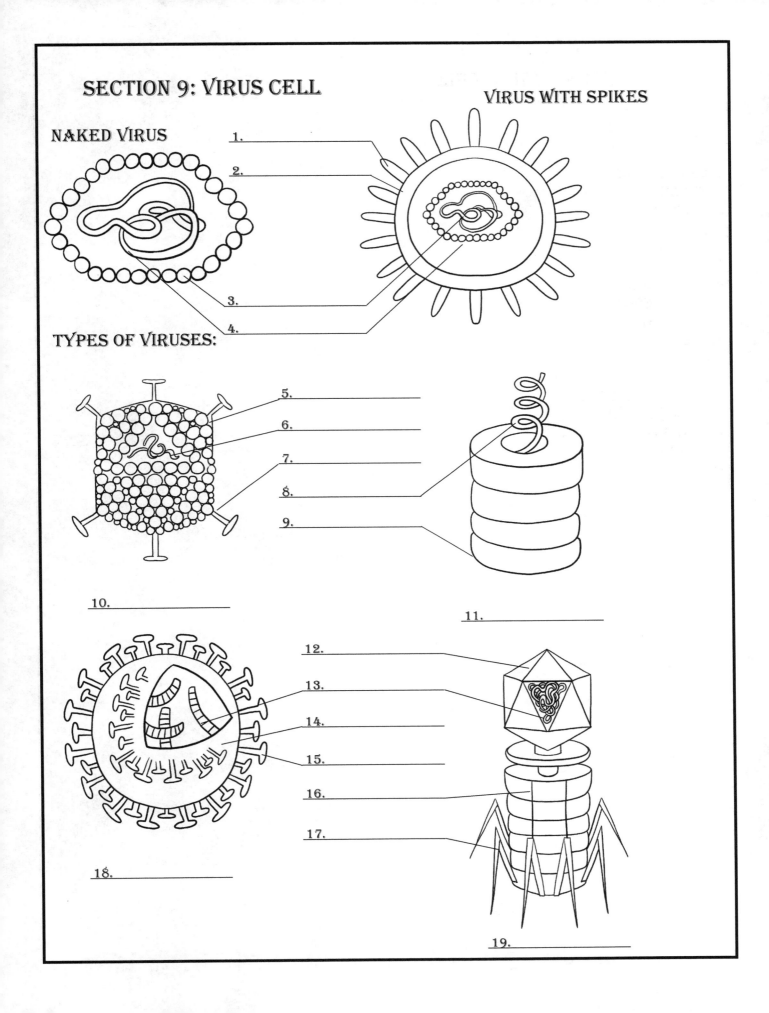

SECTION 9: VIRUS CELL

VIRUS WITH SPIKES

NAKED VIRUS

1. _____
2. _____

3. _____
4. _____

TYPES OF VIRUSES:

5. _____
6. _____
7. _____
8. _____
9. _____

10. _____

11. _____

12. _____
13. _____
14. _____
15. _____
16. _____
17. _____

18. _____

19. _____

SECTION 9: VIRUS CELL

1. SPIKE
2. ENVELOPE
3. CAPSOMERE
4. NUCLEIC ACID
5. CAPSOMERE
6. DNA
7. GLYCOPROTEIN
8. RNA
9. CAPSOMERE
10. POLYHEDRAL
11. HELICAL
12. HEAD
13. DNA
14. CAPSID
15. GLYCOPROTEIN
16. TAIL SHEATH
17. TAIL FIBER
18. SPHERICAL
19. COMPLEX

SECTION 10: VIRUS TYPES

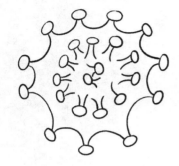

1. _____

2. _____

3. _____

4. _____

5. _____

6 _____

7. _____

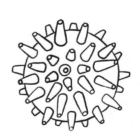

8. _____

9. _____

10. _____

SECTION 10: VIRUS TYPES

1. HIV
2. HEPATITIS B
3. EBOLA
4. ADENOVIRUS
5. INFLUENZA
6. RABIES
7. PAPILLOMAVIRUS
8. ROTAVIRUS
9. HERPES
10. BACTERIOPHAGE

SECTION 11: INFLUENZA VIRUS

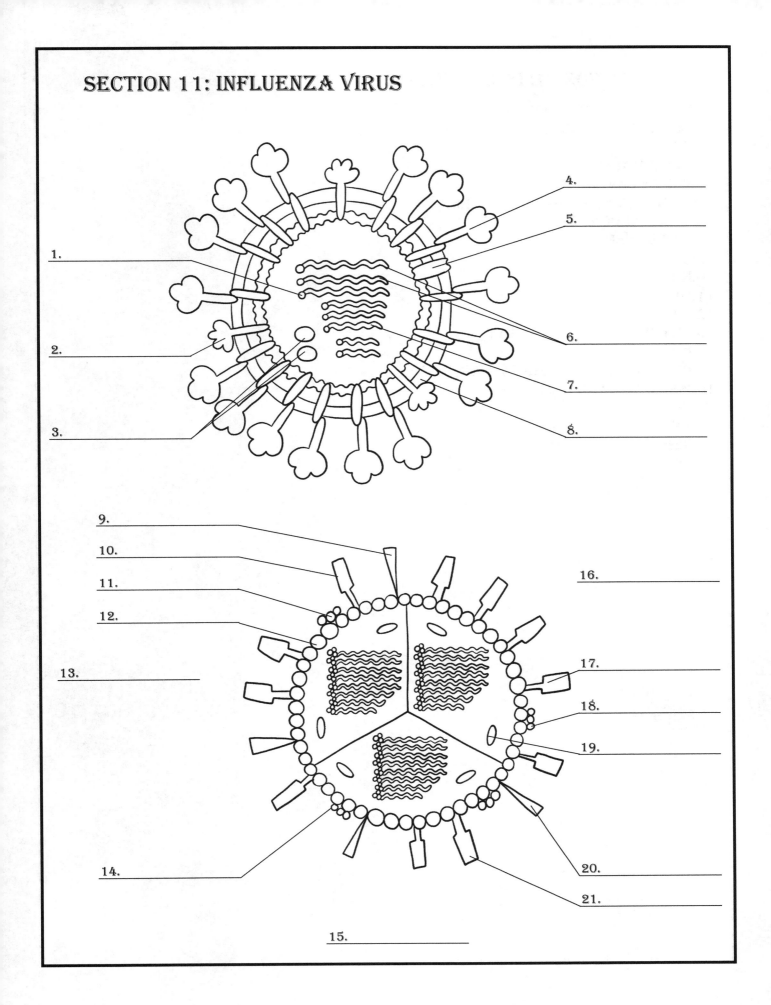

1.
2.
3.
4.
5.
6.
7.
8.
9.
10.
11.
12.
13.
14.
15.
16.
17.
18.
19.
20.
21.

SECTION 11: INFLUENZA VIRUS

1. PB1, PB2, PA (RNA POLYMERASE)
2. NA (NEURAAMINIDASE)
3. NEP
4. HA (HEMAGGLUTININ)
5. M2 (ION CHANNEL)
6. SEGMENTED (-) STRAND RNA GENE
7. NP (NUCLEOCAPSID PROTEIN)
8. LIPID LAYER
9. NA
10. HA
11. M2
12. M1
13. INFLUENZA A H1-18 N1-N11
14. M2
15. INFLUENZA B YAMAGATA & VICTORIA
16. INFLUENZA C HEF
17. HEF
18. M2
19. NEP
20. NA
21. HA

SECTION 12: BACTERIOPHAGE VIRUS

ANIMAL VIRUS

1. _____

2. _____

BACTERIOPHAGE

3. _____

4. _____

5. _____

6. _____

7. _____

8. _____

9. _____

SECTION 12: BACTERIOPHAGE VIRUS

1.DNA
2.CAPSID
3.HEAD
4.DNA
5.NECK
6.TAIL SHEATH
7.END PLATE
8.TAIL FIBERS
9.PIN

SECTION 13: HIV VIRUS

1. _____

2. _____

3. _____

4. _____

5. _____

SECTION 13: HIV VIRUS

1. CAPSID
2. GLYCOPROTEIN
3. VIRAL ENVELOPE
4. REVERSE TRANSCRIPTASE ENZYME
5. IDENTICAL RNA STRANDS

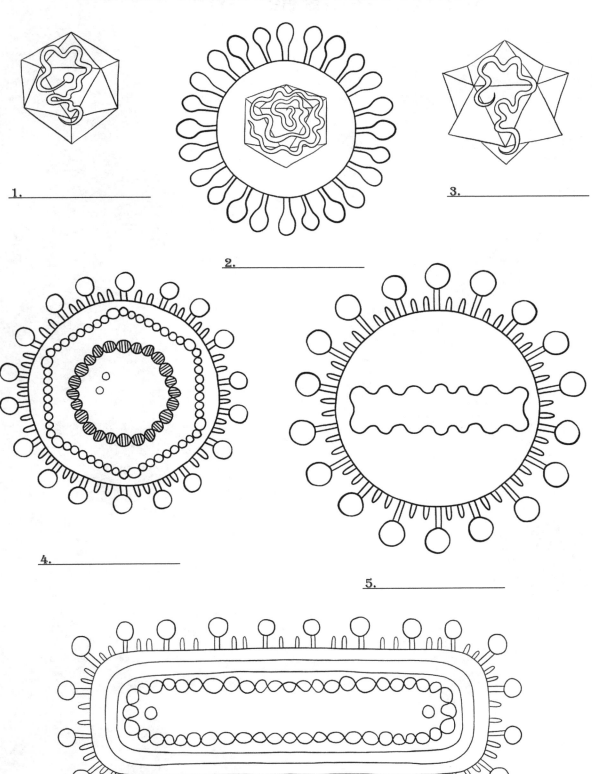

1. _____

2. _____

3. _____

4. _____

5. _____

6. _____

SECTION 14: HEPATITIS VIRUS TYPES

1. HEPATITIS A
2. HEPATITIS C
3. HEPATITIS E
4. HEPATITIS B
5. HEPATITIS D
6. HEPATITIS B

SECTION 15: HEPATITIS VIRUS

HEPATITIS B VIRUS

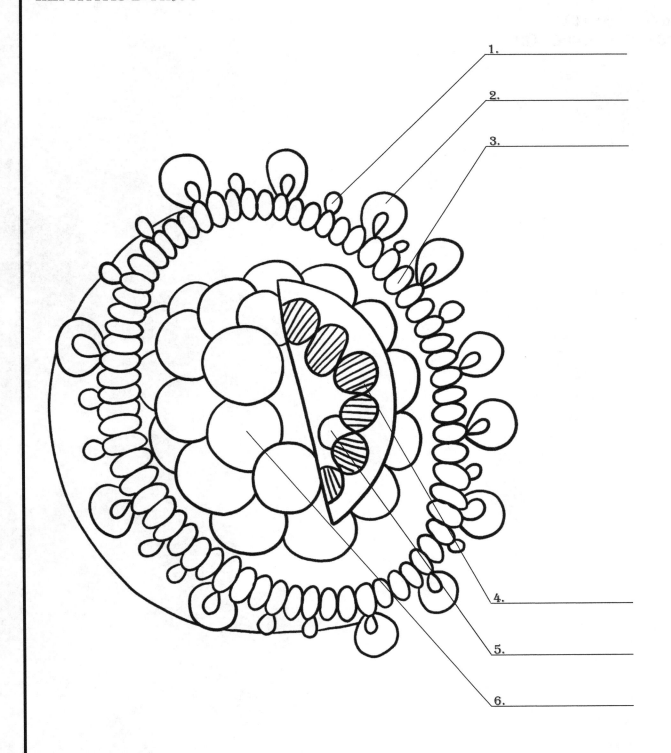

1. _____

2. _____

3. _____

4. _____

5. _____

6. _____

SECTION 15: HEPATITIS VIRUS

1. MEDIUM SURFACE PROTEIN (S+PRES2)
2. LARGE SURFACE PROTEIN (S+PRES1)
3. SMALL SURFACE PROTEIN (S)
4. DNA
5. POLYMEROSE (P)
6. ICOSAHEDRAL CORE (C)

SECTION 16: CORONA VIRUS

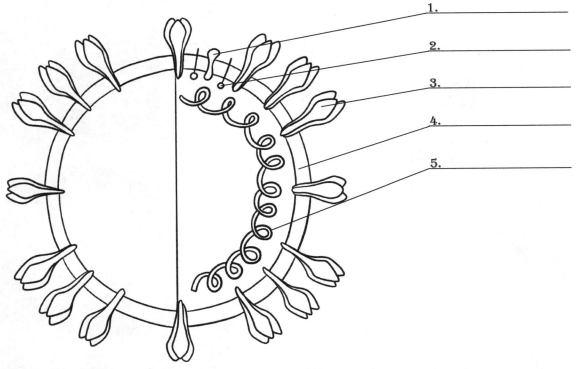

1. _____
2. _____
3. _____
4. _____
5. _____

CORONA VIRUS BALTIMORE GROUP N ((+)SSRNA)

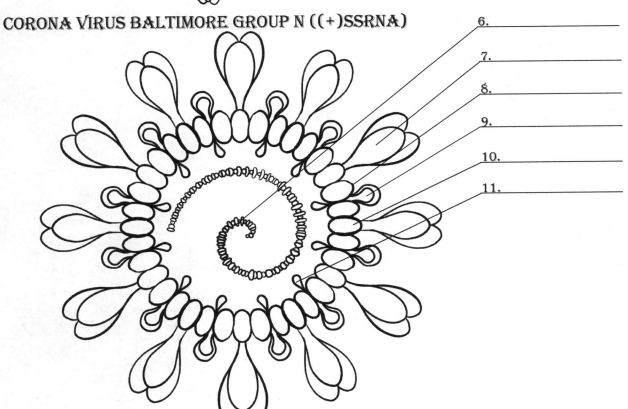

6. _____
7. _____
8. _____
9. _____
10. _____
11. _____

SECTION 16: CORONA VIRUS

1. HEMMAGLUTININ-ESTERASE
2. M-PROTEIN
3. SPIKE GLYCOPROTEIN
4. ENVELOPE
5. (+)SSRNA AND N-PROTEIN (NUCLEOCAPSID)
6. RNA +NUCLEOPROTEIN N
7. GLYCOPROTEIN SPIKES
8. LIPID BILAYER MEMBRANE
9. HEMMAGLUTININ ESTERASE
10. MEMBRANε PROTEIN M
11. ENVELOPE SMALL MEMBRANE PROTEIN E

SECTION 17: EBOLA VIRUS

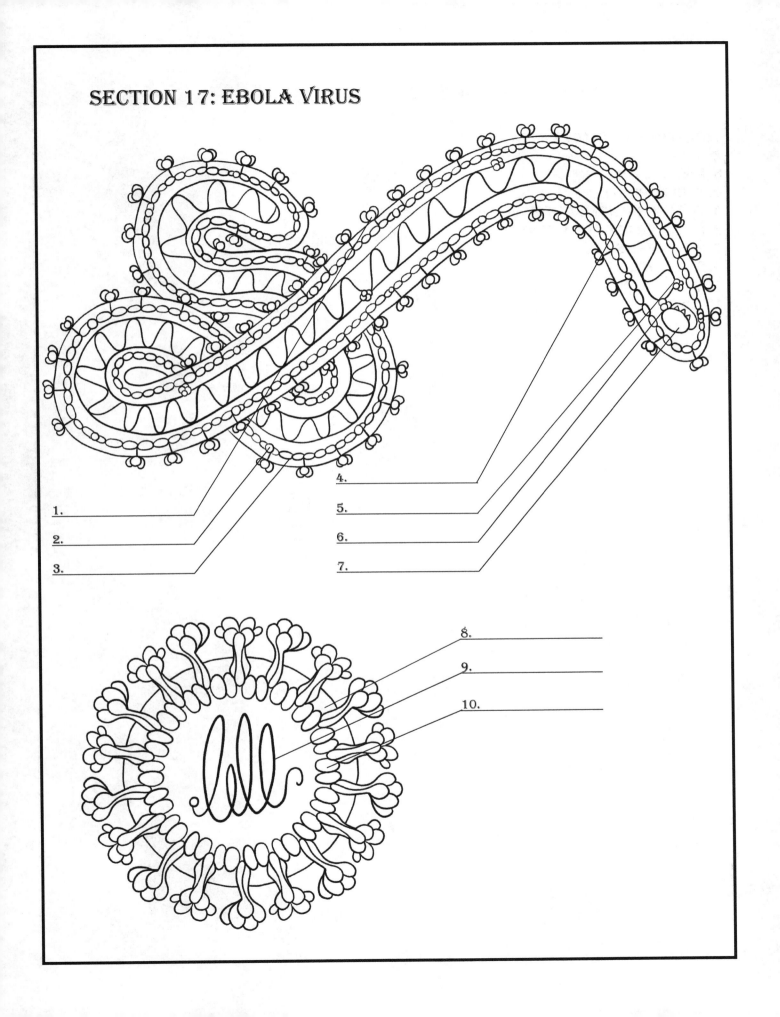

1. _____
2. _____
3. _____
4. _____
5. _____
6. _____
7. _____
8. _____
9. _____
10. _____

SECTION 17: EBOLA VIRUS

1. GLYCOPROTEIN (GP)
2. VP24
3. MATRIX VP40
4. NUCLEOPROTEIN (N)
5. TRANSCRIPTION FACTOR VP30
6. POLYMERASE COFACTOR VP35
7. POLYMERASE (L)
8. ENVELOPE
9. RNA
10. CAPSID

SECTION 18: ADENOVIRUS

ADENO VIRUS BALTIMORE GROUP I (DSDNA)

1.
2.
3.
4.
5.
6.
7.
8.
9.
10.
11.
12.
13.
14.

SECTION 18: ADENOVIRUS

1. FIBERS
2. PENTON PASE
3. PENTON MINOR PROTEIN IMA
4. HEXOM MINOR PROTEIN VI
5. DNA
6. NUCLOPROTEIN IVA2
7. GENOM TERMINAL PROTEIN
8. NUCLEOPROTEIN MU
9. PROTEASE
10. CORE PROTEIN VII
11. HEXOM MINOR PROTEIN VI
12. HEXOM MINOR PROTEIN IX
13. CORE PROTEIN V
14. HEXOM MINOR PROTEIN VIII

SECTION 19: MEASLES VIRUS

1.

2.

3.

4.

5.

6.

7.

8.

SECTION 19: MEASLES VIRUS

1. NUCLEOCAPSID
2. PHOSPHOPROTEIN
3. LARGE PROTEIN
4. LIPID BILAYER
5. RNA
6. MATRIX
7. FUSION
8. HAEMAGGLUTIN

SECTION 20: ROTAVIRUS

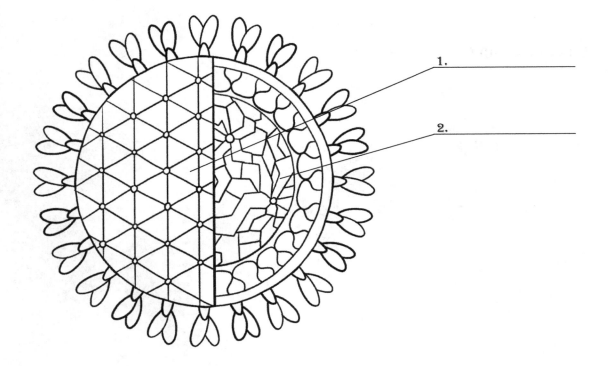

1. _____

2. _____

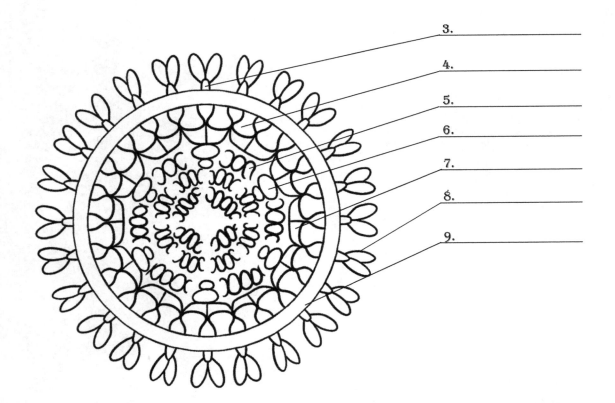

3. _____

4. _____

5. _____

6. _____

7. _____

8. _____

9. _____

SECTION 20: ROTAVIRUS

1. T=13 INTERMEDIATE CAPSID
2. T=12 INNER CAPSID
3. VP5
4. INTERMEDIATE CAPSID PROTEIN VP6
5. RNA
6. RDRP VP1, VP3
7. VP2
8. VP8
9. OUTER CAPSID PROTEIN

SECTION 21: VARICELLA VIRUS

1. _____

2. _____

3. _____

4. _____

5. _____

SECTION 21: VARICELLA VIRUS

1. LIPID ENVELOPE
2. TEGUMENT
3. NUCLEOCAPSID
4. DOUBLE STRAND DNA GENOME
5. GLYCOPROTEIN SPIKE

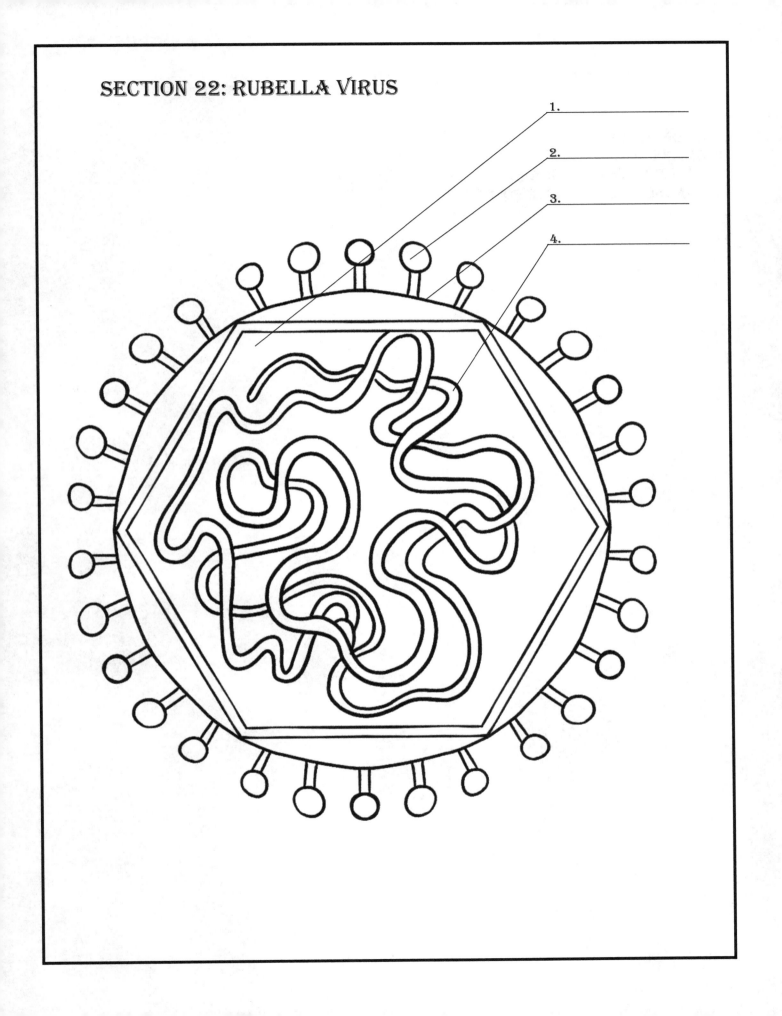

1. _____

2. _____

3. _____

4. _____

SECTION 22: RUBELLA VIRUS

1. ICOSAHEDRAL NUCLEOCAPSID
2. GLYCOPROTEIN
3. LIPID BILAYER MEMBRANE
4. RNA (SINGLE-STRANDED POSITIVE SENSE)

SECTION 23: PLASMODIUM

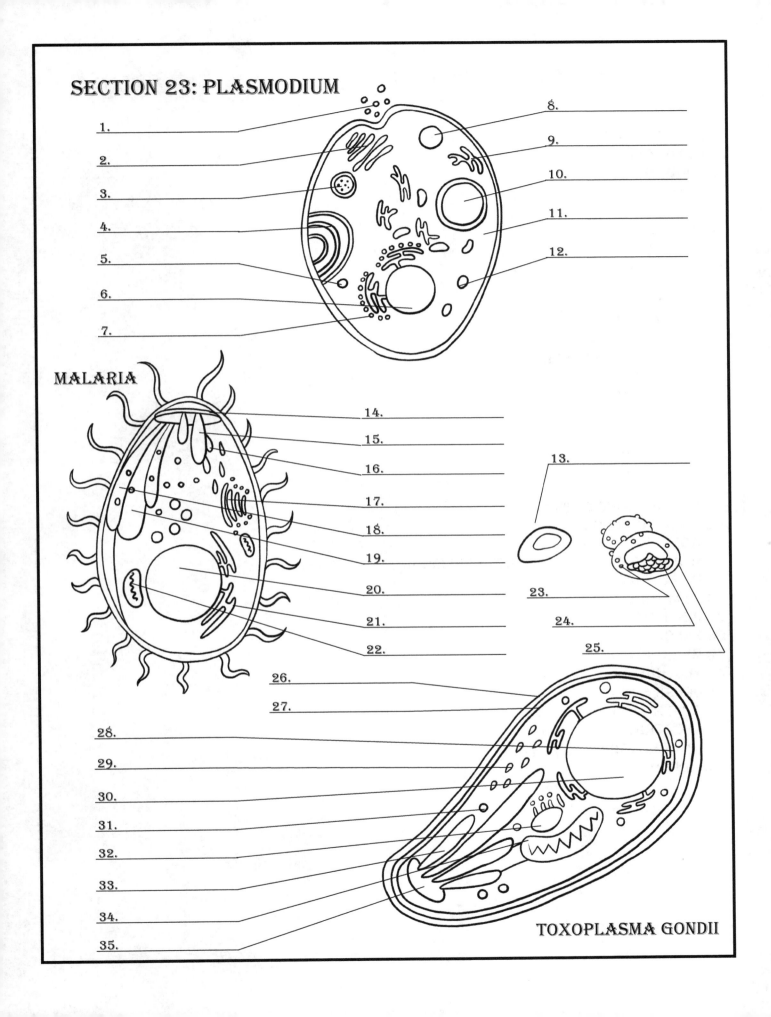

1. _____
2. _____
3. _____
4. _____
5. _____
6. _____
7. _____

8. _____
9. _____
10. _____
11. _____
12. _____

MALARIA

14. _____
15. _____
16. _____
17. _____
18. _____
19. _____
20. _____
21. _____
22. _____

13. _____

23. _____
24. _____
25. _____

26. _____
27. _____
28. _____
29. _____
30. _____
31. _____
32. _____
33. _____
34. _____
35. _____

TOXOPLASMA GONDII

SECTION 23: PLASMODIUM

1. PINOCYTIC VESICLES
2. GOLGI APPARATUS
3. FOOD VACUOLE
4. CONCENTRIC BODY
5. RIBOSOME
6. NUCLEUS
7. ROUND ER
8. HEMOZOIN
9. SMOOTH ER
10. VACUOLE
11. CYTOPLASM
12. MITOCHONDRION
13. NORMAL BLOOD CELL
14. POLAR RINGS
15. RHOPTRIES
16. MICRONEME
17. GOLGI APPARATUS
18. MICROTUBULE
19. APICOPLAST
20. NUCLEUS
21. ENDOPLASMIC RETICULUM
22. MITOCHONDRION
23. ADHESIVE KNOB
24. MALARIA PARASITES MULTIPLIED IN RBC
25. INFECTED BLOOD CELL
26. PLASMA MEMBRANE
27. INNER MEMBRANE
28. ENDOPLASMIC RETICULUM
29. MICRONEMES
30. NUCLEUS
31. DENSE GRANULE
32. APICOPLAST
33. RHOPTRIES
34. MITOCHONDRION
35. CONOID

SECTION 24: B-CELL AND T-CELL ACTIVATION

T-CELL ACTIVATION

4. _____

1. _____   2. _____   3. _____

5. _____

6. _____   8. _____   9. _____

7. _____

10. _____

B-CELL ACTIVATION

12. _____   14. _____

11. _____   13. _____

15. _____

18. _____   19. _____

16. _____

17. _____

SECTION 24: B-CELL AND T-CELL ACTIVATION

1. VIRUS
2. MACROPHAGE
3. ANTIGEN
4. HELPER T-CELL
5. CYTOTOXIC T-CELL
6. INFECTED CELL DESTRUCTION
7. T-CELL ACTIVATION
8. INFECTED CELL
9. INTERLUKIN
10. REPLICATION
11. VIRUS
12. ANTIGEN
13. B-CELL (NATIVE)
14. B-CELL ACTIVATION
15. LYMPHOBLAST
16. ANTIBODY
17. MEMORY B-CELL
18. PLASMA CELL
19. B-CELL

SECTION 25: IMMUNE SYSTEM CELLS

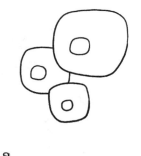

3. _____

2. _____

1. _____

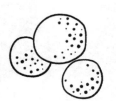

6. _____

5. _____

4. _____

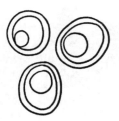

7. _____

8. _____

9. _____

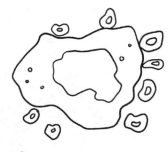

10. _____

11. _____

SECTION 25: IMMUNE SYSTEM CELLS

1. DENDRITIC CELLS
2. INNATE LYMPHOID
3. T CELLS
4. NATURAL KILLERS (NK) CELLS
5. MYCLOID- DERIVED SUPPRESSOR CELLS (MDSC)
6. PLATELETS
7. THYMOCYTES
8. B CELLS
9. GRANULOCYTES
10. MEGATARYOCYTES
11. RED BLOOD CELLS (RBCS)

SECTION 26: ANTIBACTERIAL DRUGS

ANTIBIOTIC RESISTANCE MECHANISMS

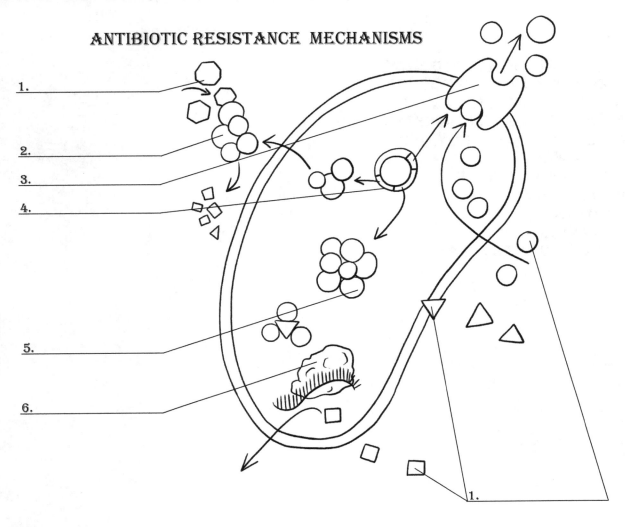

1.

2.

3.

4.

5.

6.

1.

ANTIBACTERIAL DRUGS

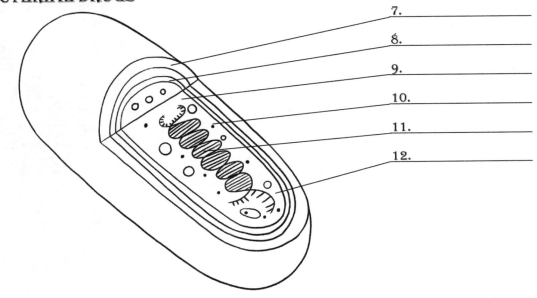

7.

8.

9.

10.

11.

12.

SECTION 26: ANTIBACTERIAL DRUGS

1. ANTIBIOTICS
2. ANTIBIOTIC-DEGRADING ENZYME
3. EFFLUX PUMP
4. ANTIBIOTIC-RESISTENCE GENES
5. ANTIBIOTIC- ALTERING ENZYME
6. ALTERED ANTIBIOTIC TARGET
7. CELL WALL
8. PLASMA MEMBRANE
9. CYTOPLASM
10. RIBOSOME
11. DNA SYNTHESIS
12. METABOLIC PATHWAYS

SECTION 27: COMMON CONTAMINANT FUNGI

RHIZOPUS

1. _____

2. _____

3. _____

4. _____

5. _____

6. _____

7. _____

8. _____

9. _____

10. _____

11. _____

12. _____

13. _____

14. _____

15. _____

MUCOR

ASPERGILLUS

16. _____

SECTION 27: COMMON CONTAMINANT FUNGI

1. SPORANGIUM
2. COLUMELLA (FEEDS SPORES)
3. APOPHYSIS
4. SPORANGIOPHORE
5. MYCELIUM
6. SPORE
7. STOLON
8. RHIZOID
9. HYPHA

CPSIA information can be obtained
at www.ICGtesting.com
Printed in the USA
LVHW061401070422
715594LV00007B/164

9 781914 207549